# How many?

▶ **Count and write the number.**

2

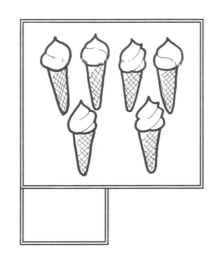

▶ **Write numbers 0 – 10**

| 0 | 1 |  |  |  |  |  |  |  |  |  |
|---|---|---|---|---|---|---|---|---|---|---|

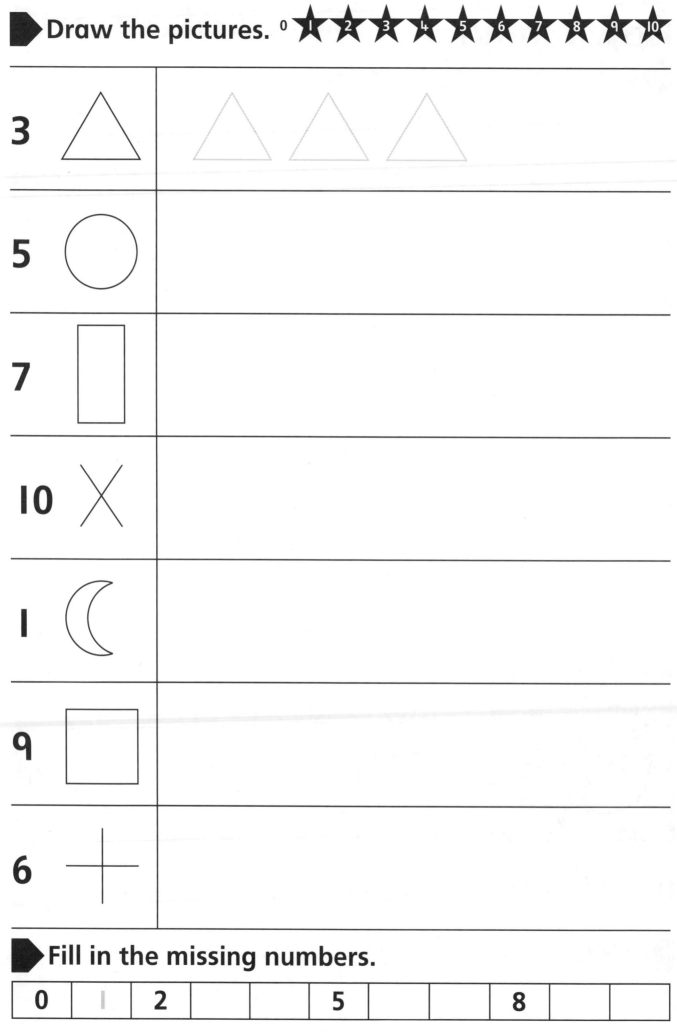

▶ **Draw the pictures.** 0 ★ 1 ★ 2 ★ 3 ★ 4 ★ 5 ★ 6 ★ 7 ★ 8 ★ 9 ★ 10

| | |
|---|---|
| **3** △ | △ △ △ |
| **5** ○ | |
| **7** ▭ | |
| **10** ✕ | |
| **I** ☾ | |
| **9** ▢ | |
| **6** ✚ | |

▶ **Fill in the missing numbers.**

| 0 | I | 2 | | | 5 | | | 8 | | |
|---|---|---|---|---|---|---|---|---|---|---|

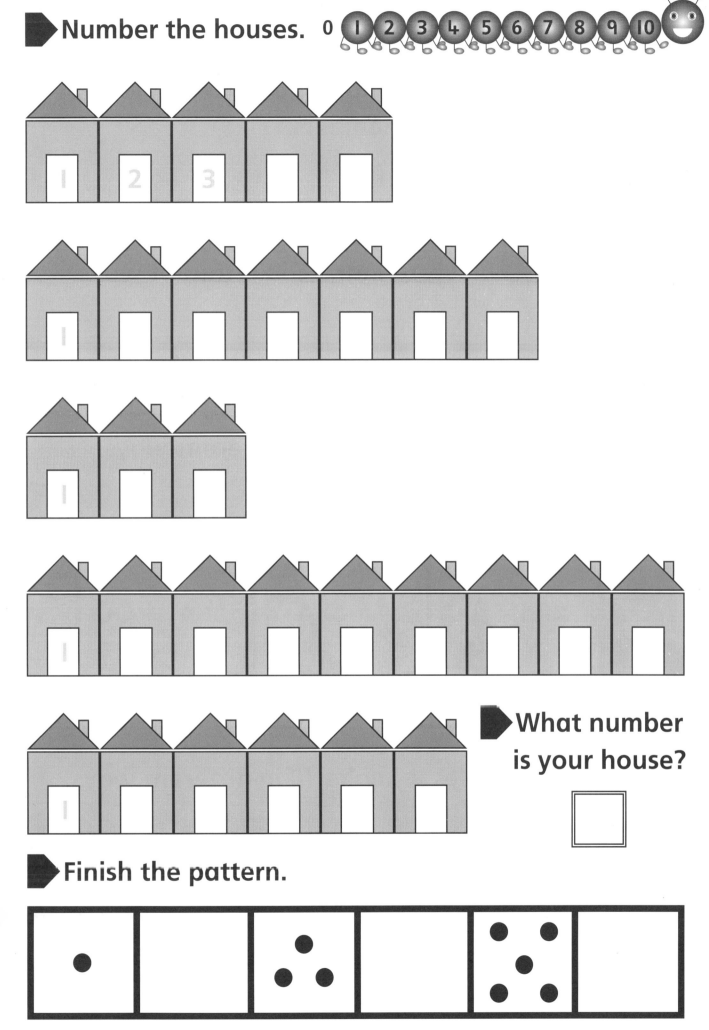

**Number the houses.** 0 1 2 3 4 5 6 7 8 9 10

**What number is your house?**

**Finish the pattern.**

5

**Colour the wheels to make 4 in different ways. Write the numbers.**

| 3 + 1 | + | + | + |
|-------|---|---|---|

**Colour the wheels to make 6 in different ways.**

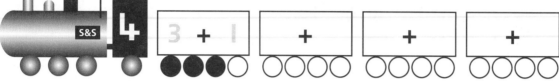

| 2 + 4 | + | + | + | + |
|-------|---|---|---|---|

**Colour the flags to make 8 in different ways.**

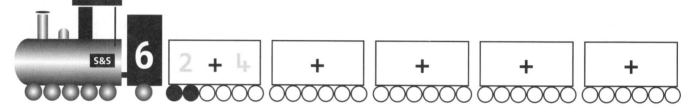

8 — 1 + 7  8 — +  8 — +  8 — +

**Colour the apples to make 10 in different ways.**

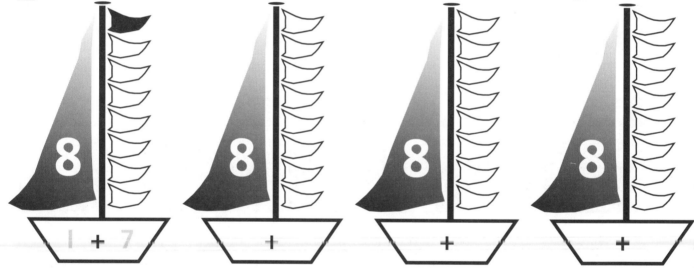

4 + 6 → 10   + → 10   + → 10   + → 10

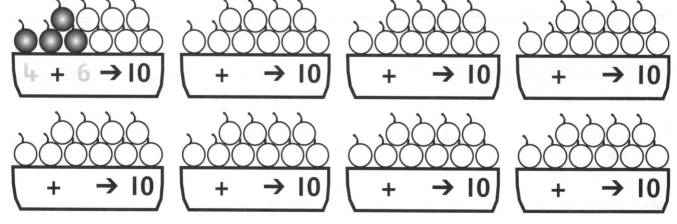

+ → 10   + → 10   + → 10   + → 10

6

**How many pennies?** 1p 1p 1p 1p 1p 1p 1p 1p 1p 1p

Emma has 4p  Jo has  Seema has  Asif has

**Put a ✓ by the child who has the most money.**

7

## Colour the number of pennies.

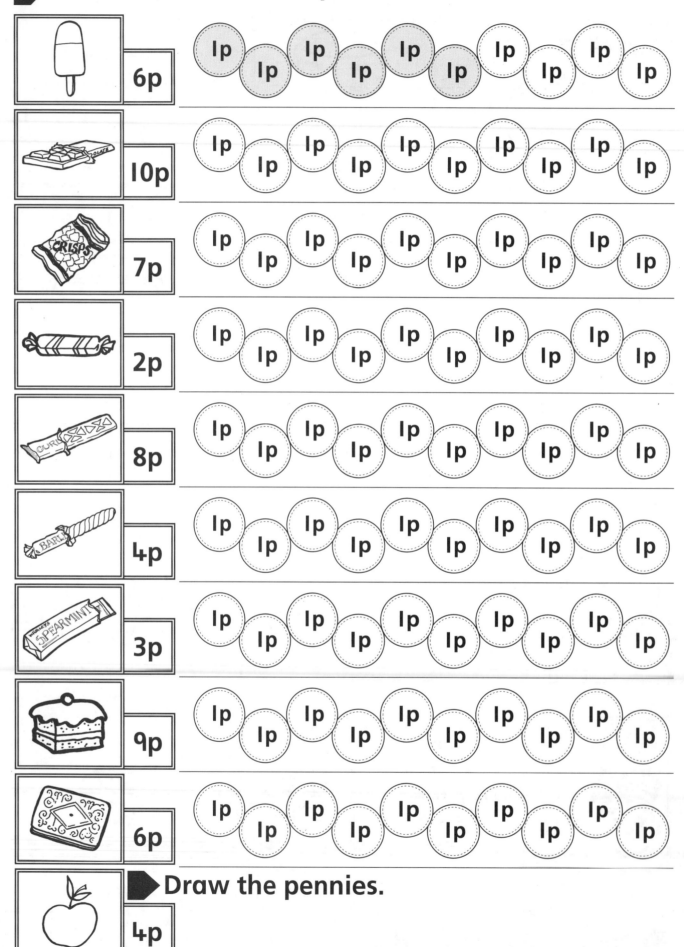

Draw the pennies.

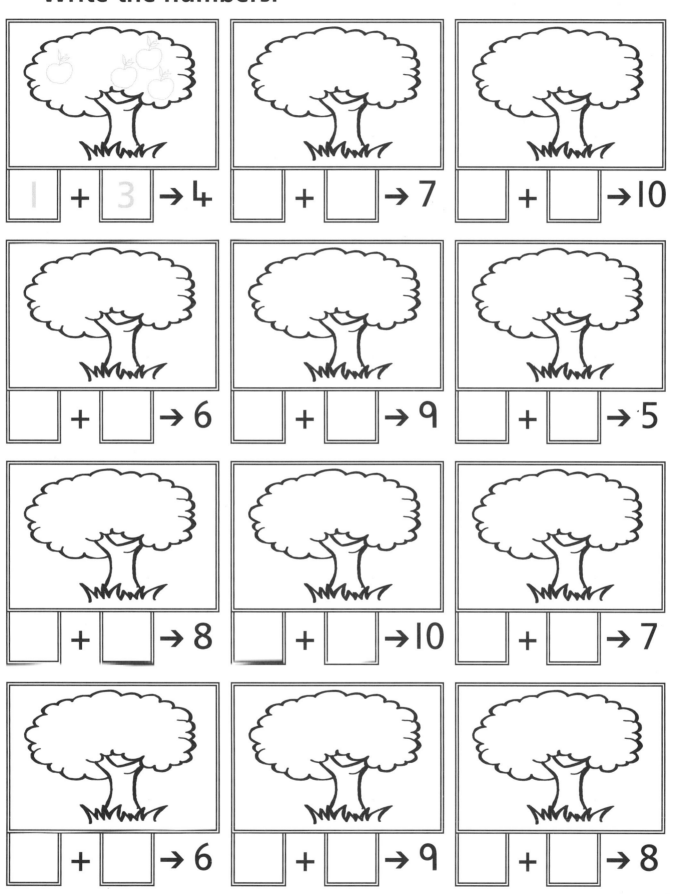

| | | | | | |
|---|---|---|---|---|---|
| 1 | + | 3 | → 4 | | |
| ☐ | + | ☐ | → 7 | | |
| ☐ | + | ☐ | → 10 | | |

| | + | | → 6 |
| | + | | → 9 |
| | + | | → 5 |

| | + | | → 8 |
| | + | | → 10 |
| | + | | → 7 |

| | + | | → 6 |
| | + | | → 9 |
| | + | | → 8 |

► **How many different sums did you make?** ☐

9

**Draw the stars.**

**Write the number.**

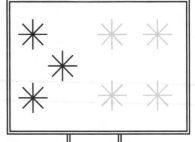

3 + 4 → 7

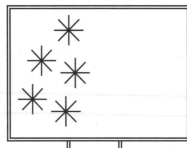

5 + ☐ → 9

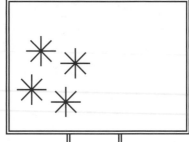

4 + ☐ → 6

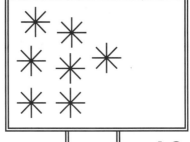

7 + ☐ → 10

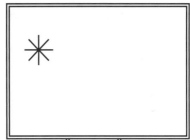

1 + ☐ → 8

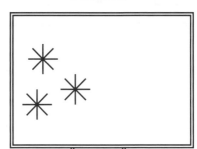

3 + ☐ → 5

6 + ☐ → 8

4 + ☐ → 5

2 + ☐ → 7

7 + ☐ → 9

3 + ☐ → 6

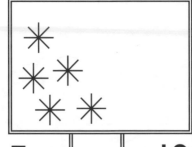

5 + ☐ → 10

**Draw the missing spots to make ten.**

 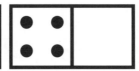 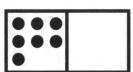 

# Fat and thin

▶ **Ring the thinner one.**

 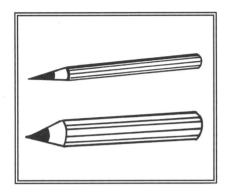 

▶ **Ring the fatter one.**

  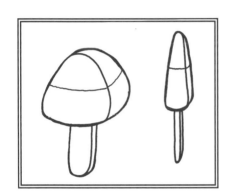

▶ **Draw 3 things thicker than a**

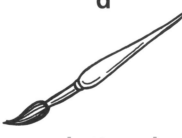

**paintbrush.**

▶ **Draw 3 things thinner than a**

**cuddly toy.**

# Long and short

▶ **Ring the shorter one.**

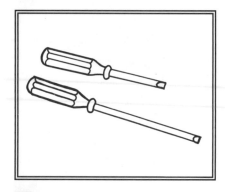
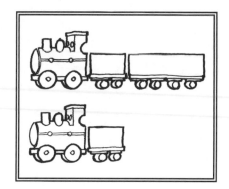
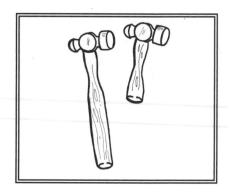

▶ **Ring the longer one.**

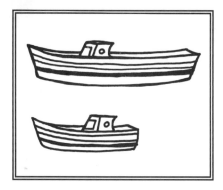
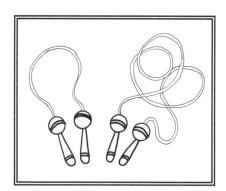

▶ **Draw 3 things longer than a**

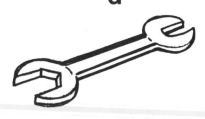

**spanner.**

▶ **Draw 3 things shorter than a**

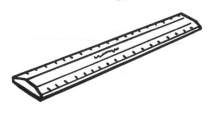

**ruler.**

# Time

▶ **Colour the hands on the clocks.**
Use red for the hour hand and blue for the minute hand.
▶ **Write the time in the box.**

*7* o'clock

o'clock

o'clock

o'clock

o'clock

o'clock

o'clock

o'clock

o'clock

o'clock

o'clock

o'clock

# Time

▶ **Draw the hands on the clocks.**
Use red for the hour hand and blue for the minute hand.

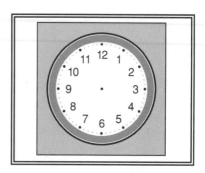

1 o'clock

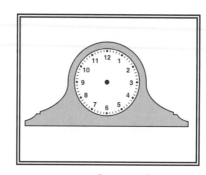

7 o'clock

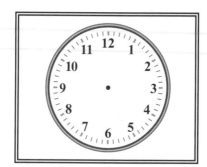

3 o'clock

11 o'clock

2 o'clock

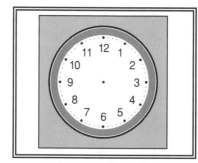

9 o'clock

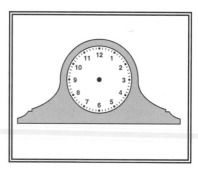

4 o'clock

8 o'clock

5 o'clock

10 o'clock

6 o'clock

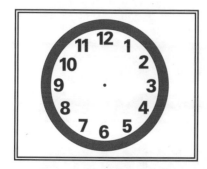

12 o'clock

# Count and write.

How many toys?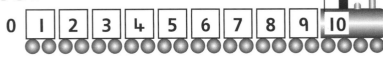

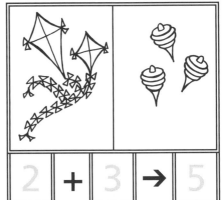

2 + 3 → 5

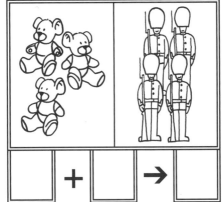

◻ + ◻ → ◻

◻ + ◻ → ◻

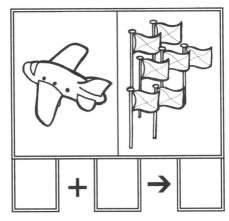

◻ + ◻ → ◻

◻ + ◻ → ◻

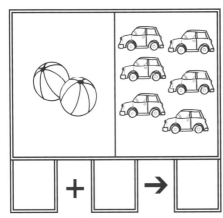

◻ + ◻ → ◻

◻ + ◻ → ◻

◻ + ◻ → ◻

◻ + ◻ → ◻

◻ + ◻ → ◻

◻ + ◻ → ◻

◻ + ◻ → ◻

15

# Dice Game

▶ Make a dice using these numbers 0 0 1 2 3 4.
Throw your dice to make the sum.

6 + ☐ → ☐     3 + ☐ → ☐     4 + ☐ → ☐

2 + ☐ → ☐     5 + ☐ → ☐     5 + ☐ → ☐

3 + ☐ → ☐     1 + ☐ → ☐     3 + ☐ → ☐

5 + ☐ → ☐     2 + ☐ → ☐     6 + ☐ → ☐

▶ Now use two dice to make up your own sums.

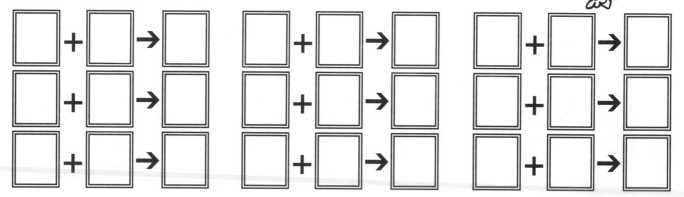

☐ + ☐ → ☐     ☐ + ☐ → ☐     ☐ + ☐ → ☐

☐ + ☐ → ☐     ☐ + ☐ → ☐     ☐ + ☐ → ☐

☐ + ☐ → ☐     ☐ + ☐ → ☐     ☐ + ☐ → ☐

▶ Find two numbers to complete the sum.

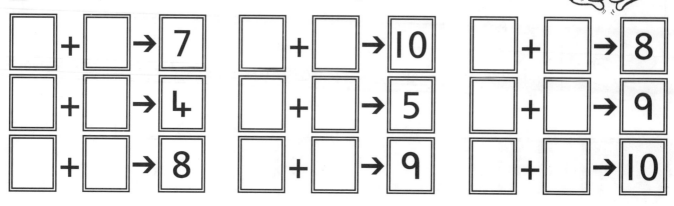

☐ + ☐ → 7     ☐ + ☐ → 10     ☐ + ☐ → 8

☐ + ☐ → 4     ☐ + ☐ → 5     ☐ + ☐ → 9

☐ + ☐ → 8     ☐ + ☐ → 9     ☐ + ☐ → 10

# How many animals?

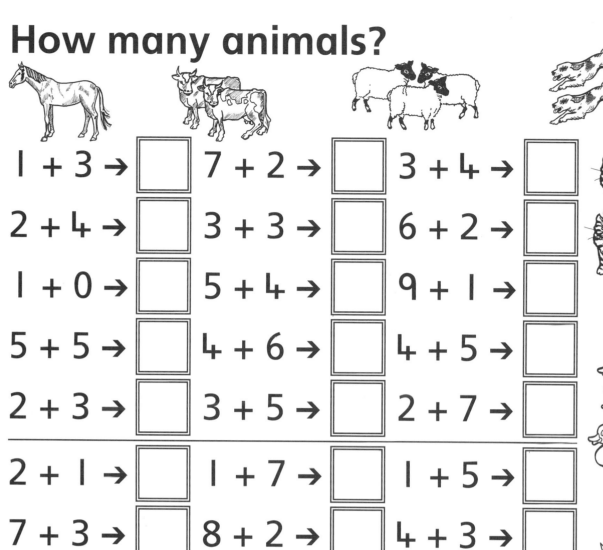

| 1 + 3 → ☐ | 7 + 2 → ☐ | 3 + 4 → ☐ |
| 2 + 4 → ☐ | 3 + 3 → ☐ | 6 + 2 → ☐ |
| 1 + 0 → ☐ | 5 + 4 → ☐ | 9 + 1 → ☐ |
| 5 + 5 → ☐ | 4 + 6 → ☐ | 4 + 5 → ☐ |
| 2 + 3 → ☐ | 3 + 5 → ☐ | 2 + 7 → ☐ |

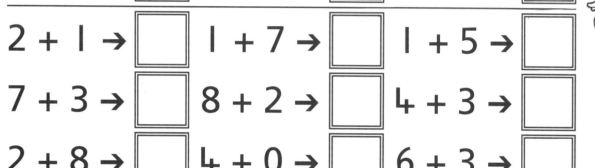

| 2 + 1 → ☐ | 1 + 7 → ☐ | 1 + 5 → ☐ |
| 7 + 3 → ☐ | 8 + 2 → ☐ | 4 + 3 → ☐ |
| 2 + 8 → ☐ | 4 + 0 → ☐ | 6 + 3 → ☐ |
| 6 + 4 → ☐ | 1 + 8 → ☐ | 8 + 0 → ☐ |
| 2 + 5 → ☐ | 4 + 4 → ☐ | 3 + 2 → ☐ |

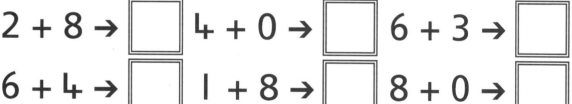

| 4 + 1 → ☐ | 5 + 3 → ☐ | 1 + 4 → ☐ |
| 1 + 6 → ☐ | 1 + 9 → ☐ | 2 + 6 → ☐ |
| 3 + 6 → ☐ | 3 + 7 → ☐ | 6 + 1 → ☐ |
| 5 + 2 → ☐ | 4 + 2 → ☐ | 2 + 2 → ☐ |
| 7 + 1 → ☐ | 1 + 2 → ☐ | 5 + 1 → ☐ |

# Picture sums

▶ **How many animals does Farmer Ted have in each field?**

2 cows + 4 sheep → 6

pigs + ducks →

horse + hens →

cats + dog →

lambs + sheep →

hens + geese →

donkey + cows →

pigs + hens →

dogs + cats →

▶ **Which field has the most animals in it?**
**Mark it with a ✓.**

▶ **How many more ducks would he put on these ponds?**
**Draw the ducks on the pond.**

6 + 2 → 8    3 + → 7    1 + → 5

18

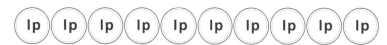

# How much does it cost?

▶ Draw the pennies.

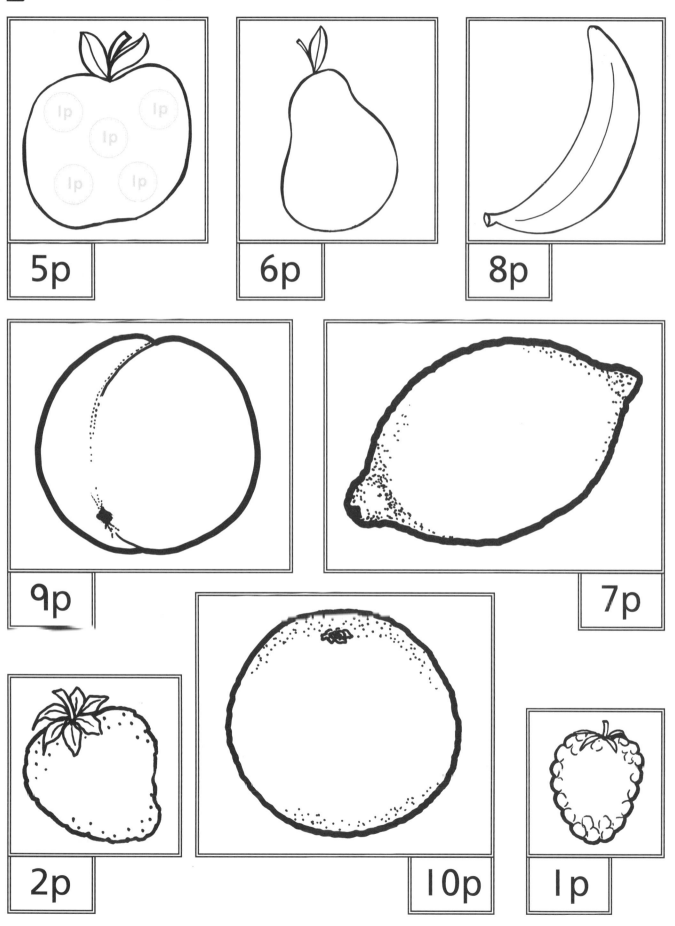

# Let's go shopping!

▶ **Buy two vegetables. Draw the pennies you spent.**

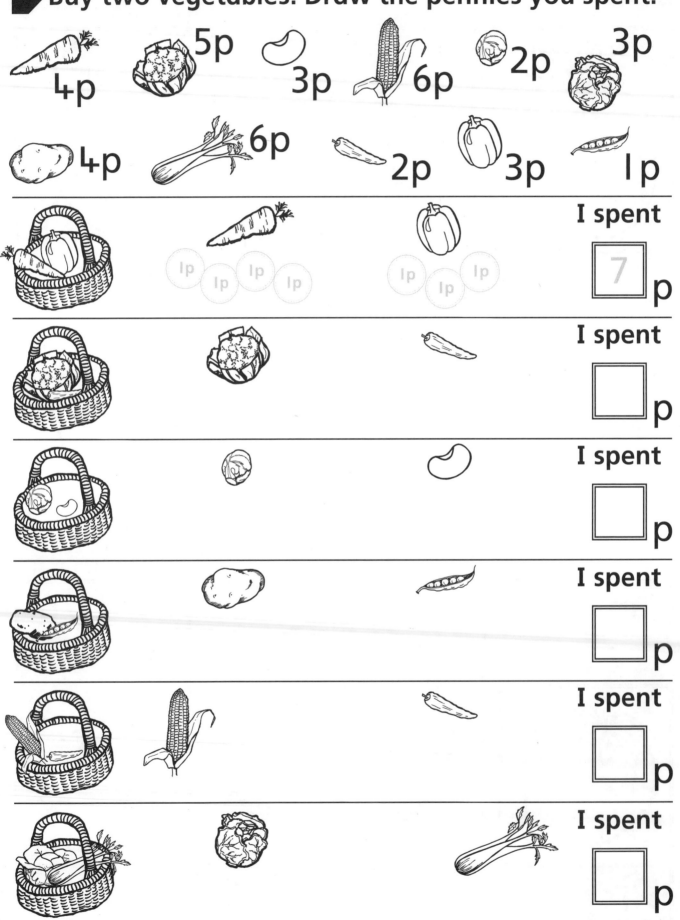

# At the Toy Shop

## How much?

▶ **Match the pennies.**

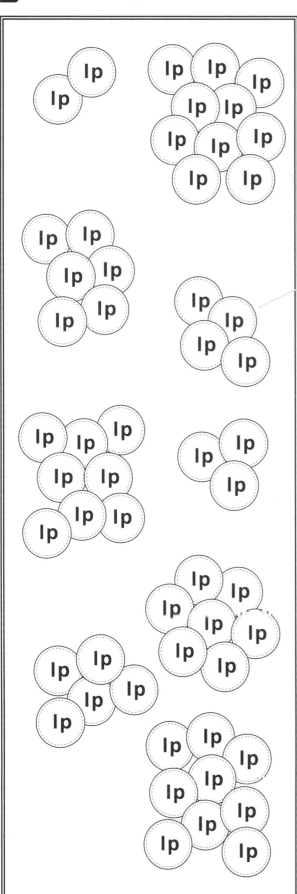

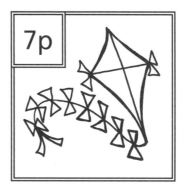
7p

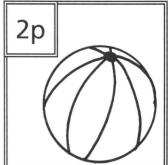
2p

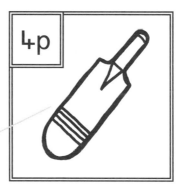
4p

6p

10p

9p

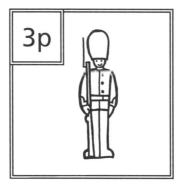
3p

8p

5p

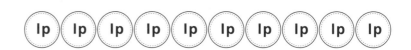

# Money Boxes

▶ **Put more money in the boxes. Draw 1p coins.**

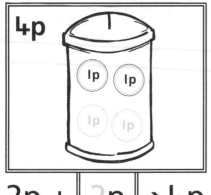

4p

2p + $\boxed{2p}$ → 4p

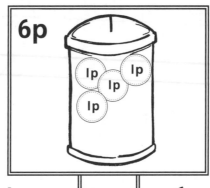

6p

4p + $\boxed{\phantom{p}\ p}$ → 6p

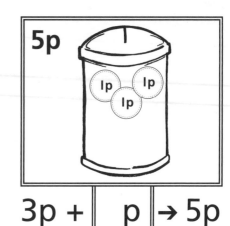

5p

3p + $\boxed{\phantom{p}\ p}$ → 5p

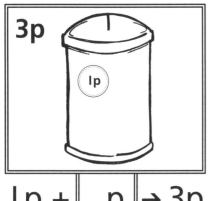

3p

1p + $\boxed{\phantom{p}\ p}$ → 3p

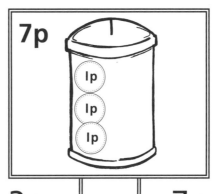

7p

3p + $\boxed{\phantom{p}\ p}$ → 7p

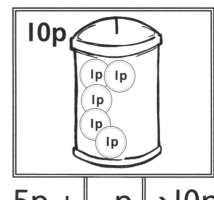

10p

5p + $\boxed{\phantom{p}\ p}$ → 10p

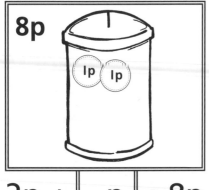

8p

2p + $\boxed{\phantom{p}\ p}$ → 8p

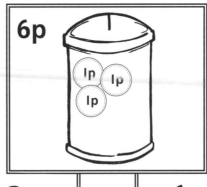

6p

3p + $\boxed{\phantom{p}\ p}$ → 6p

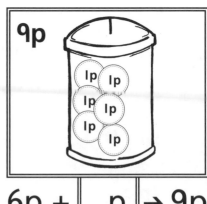

9p

6p + $\boxed{\phantom{p}\ p}$ → 9p

▶ **Draw 8p in this purse.**

# Weight

▶ **Heavier and lighter.**

Use a balance to find out which is heavier.

Ring the heavier side.

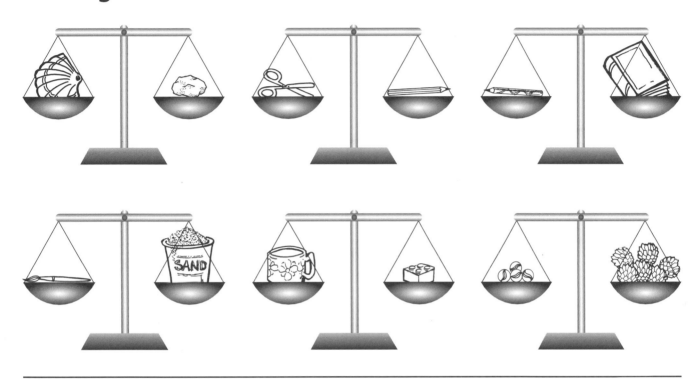

---

▶ **Use a balance to find out which is lighter.**

Ring the lighter side.

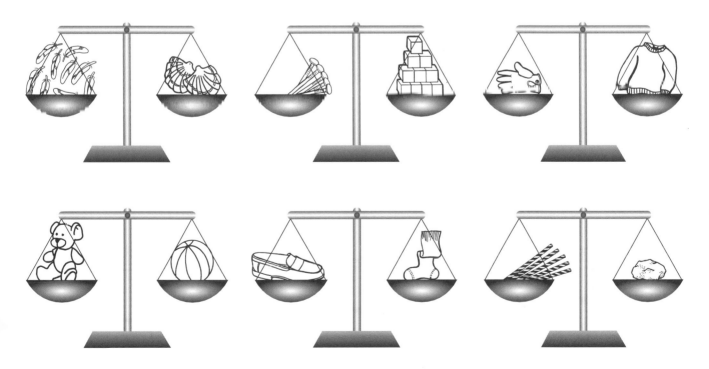

# Weight

▶ Use a balance to find 3 things lighter than your sock. Draw them.

▶ Use a balance to find 3 things heavier than your sock. Draw them.

# Shape

▶ **Colour all the squares red.**
  **Join the circles.**

▶ **Colour all the circles blue.**
  **Join the squares.**

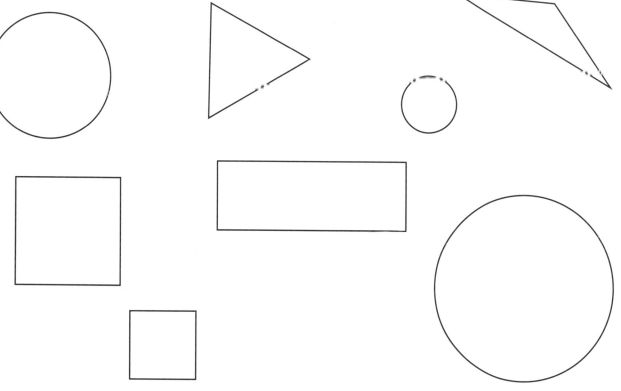

25

# Shape

▶ **Colour the triangles green.**
  **Join the rectangles.**

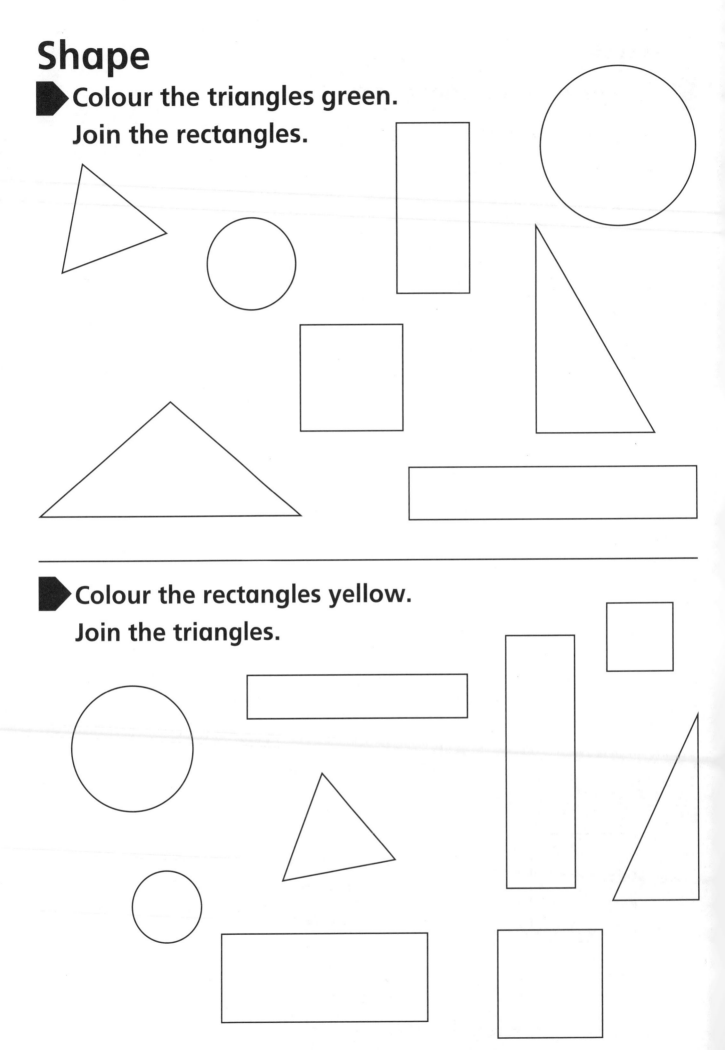

▶ **Colour the rectangles yellow.**
  **Join the triangles.**

26

# Patterns

▶ Colour the shapes.

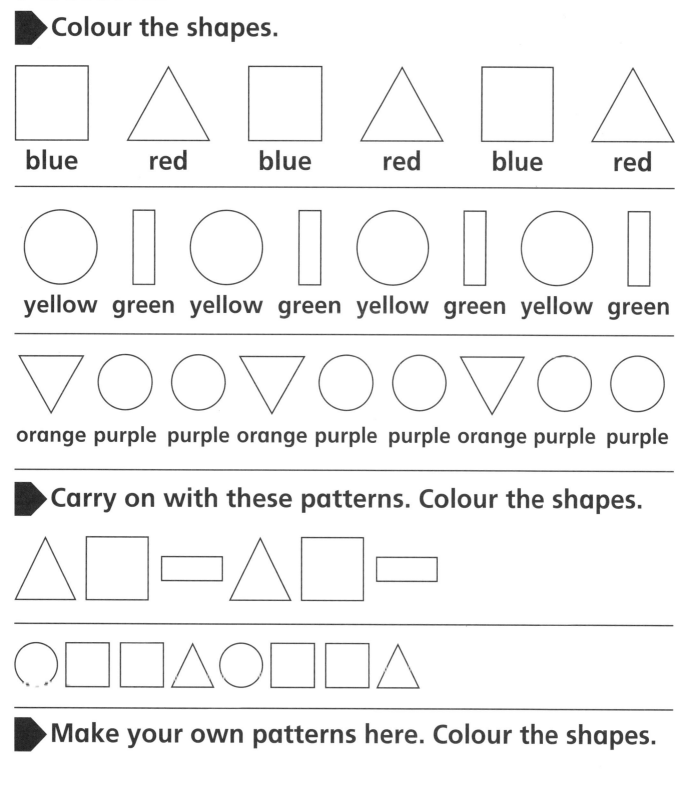

blue    red    blue    red    blue    red

yellow   green   yellow   green   yellow   green   yellow   green

orange   purple   purple   orange   purple   purple   orange   purple   purple

▶ Carry on with these patterns. Colour the shapes.

▶ Make your own patterns here. Colour the shapes.

# Patterns

▶ Carry on with these patterns. Colour them.

_____

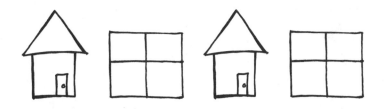

_____

_____

_____

▶ Make your own patterns here. Colour them.

_____

_____

# Patterns

▶ Finish these patterns. Colour the dots.

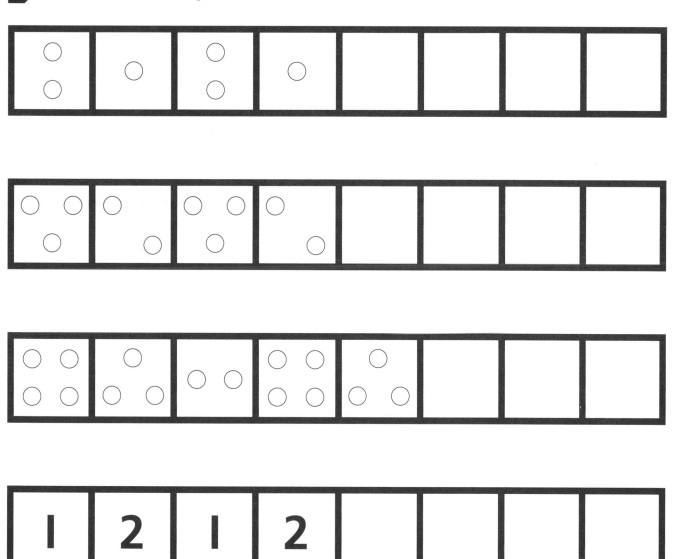

▶ Make your own patterns. Colour them.

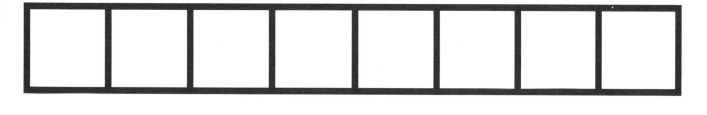

# Flower sums

▶ Make up sums on each petal to add up to the numbers in the centre of the flower.

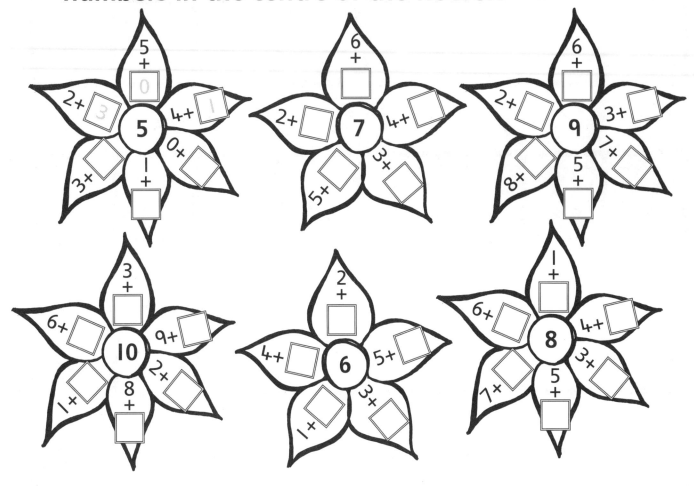

▶ Make up your own snail sums.

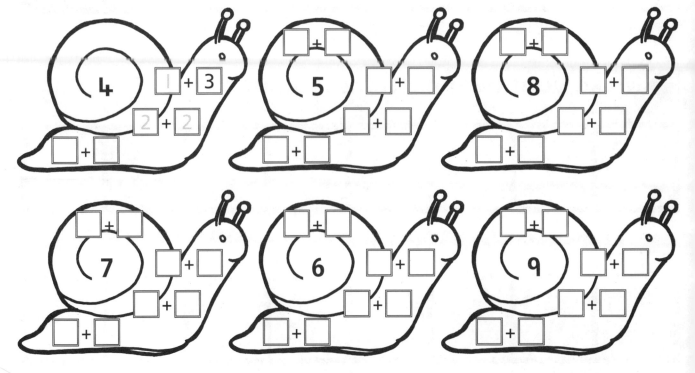

30

# Weather

▶ **What was the weather like?**

| | sunny | windy | rainy | foggy | cloudy | snowy | frosty |
|---|---|---|---|---|---|---|---|
| **4** | ☀ | | | | ☁ | | |
| **3** | ☀ | | ☂ | | ☁ | | |
| **2** | ☀ | 🪁 | ☂ | | ☁ | | |
| **1** | ☀ | 🪁 | ☂ | 🌫 | ☁ | | ❄ |

sunny   windy   rainy   foggy   cloudy   snowy   frosty

▶ **Complete:**

How many times did the sun shine? ☐

How many times was it foggy? ☐

How many times was it cloudy? ☐

How many times did it snow? ☐

How many times was it frosty? ☐

How many times did it rain? ☐

How many times was it windy? ☐

31

# Schofield & Sims
## HELPING CHILDREN TO LEARN

Schofield & Sims was established in 1901 by two headmasters and since then our name has been synonymous with educationally sound texts and teaching materials. Our mission is to publish products which are:

- Educationally sound • Good value • Written by experienced teachers
- Extensively used in schools, nurseries and play groups
- Used by parents to support their children's learning

# KEY MATHS BOOK 1

Graded maths activities for Key Stage 1.

**Key Maths Book 1** - 0 7217 0793 9     **Key Maths Book 4** - 0 7217 0796 3
**Key Maths Book 2** - 0 7217 0794 7     **Key Maths Book 5** - 0 7217 0797 1
**Key Maths Book 3** - 0 7217 0795 5

## Schofield & Sims Key Stage 1 products for 5 to 7 year olds

### Language and literacy workbooks

**Early Writing**
Books 1 - 4
Training in letter formation, leading to joined-up writing.

**Early Spellings**
Books 1 - 3
Develops spelling skills through spelling activities, spelling patterns and establishing links between reading and writing.

**Sound Practice**
Books 1 - 5
Structured practice in basic sounds.

**First Phonics**
Books 1 - 4
Develops phonic skills through carefully graded enjoyable activities.

**Basic Skills**
Books 1 - 5
Helps children to achieve literacy and extend their vocabularies.

### Maths and numeracy workbooks

**Number Books**
Books 1 - 5
Introduces basic number skills through gently graded activities.

**Times Tables**
Books 1 and 2
Straight forward tables practice.
Book 1 covers x0, x1, x2, x3, x4, x5, x10 tables
(Book 2 is for Key Stage 2).

**Posters**
Sturdy laminated posters, full colour, write-on/wipe-off, suitable for wall mounting or desk top use. Over 70 titles covering numeracy, literacy, science, nature, geography, history and languages.

# Schofield & Sims

Dogley Mill, Fenay Bridge, Huddersfield, HD8 0NQ
Phone 01484 607080    Fax 01484 606815

e-mail schofield_and_sims@compuserve.com

## Information

For further information about products for pre-school, Key Stages 1 and 2, please request our catalogue or visit our website at

**www.schofieldandsims.co.uk**

ISBN 0-7217-0793-9

9 780721 707938

**Price £1.95**
Key Stage 1
Age Range 5-7 years